A Slice of Life

A Slice of Life

Stories of Family, Friendship, Love
...and Fruitcake

FROM THE CUSTOMERS OF

COLLIN STREET BAKERY

Published by Collin Street Bakery Press

401 West Seventh Avenue

Corsicana, Texas USA

www.collinstreet.com

First Edition 2010

All original text © 2010 Collin Street Bakery Inc. All rights reserved.

"The Cowboy on the Tin" poem © 2008 Gary Penney. All rights reserved.

Illustrations © 2010 Collin Street Bakery Inc.

Cover photography by Jean Ann Bybee.

ISBN 978-0-615-36530-5

Printed in the USA

This book is dedicated to...

First, our loyal customers, without whom Collin Street Bakery would not exist.
Second, our enthusiastic staff, who take care of our customers and the business.
Third, my devoted partners, who share a common goal of
unparalleled quality of product and service.
And finally, to my mom and dad.

Like me, my father worked for his father. I asked my dad one day what it had
been like working with his father. He said, "He could not have been better to
me." I feel exactly the same about my father and mother. They could not have
been better to me.

— Bob McNutt

Contents

INTRODUCTION

It has always been our goal that every morsel of a Collin Street Bakery fruitcake be superb. So when a customer in Japan writes to tell us that the fruitcake he sent to the Himalayas arrived "in perfect quality," we know we're doing something right.

Truth be told, I always thought my family was in the bakery business. In the past few years, I've come to realize that's only the half of it. It was our customers who clued me in to what Collin Street Bakery is really about.

For years we've gotten letters from our customers. When my father was president, he got them, and before that my grandfather did. Here's one I received from Carolyn Williams, who wrote me about her much-loved father-in-law, Sherwood "Pawpa" Williams:

Throughout the years we received Pawpa's annual Christmas gift of a Collin Street Bakery fruitcake (in addition to a generous check to ensure that our three children had a good Christmas). Even those who did not typically like fruitcake looked forward to this yummy delight. When Pawpa passed away in 2004, it was fitting to continue his tradition of sending his annual Christmas gift to those he loved. The fruitcake's greeting card now reads: "In memory and honor of our Pawpa, who will live in our hearts forever."

What I've come to realize is that our fruitcakes are filled with an overflowing cup of tradition. They bring families together, connect people who are far away, make friends among former strangers. They are often the symbol of a loved one, or the assurance that family members will reunite.

It is our privilege to know we have become a part of many customers' lives. We're there for tears of both joy and sadness, for toasts and reunions, when the presents are opened and when everyone is gathered around the table.

This book is what happens when you ask customers to tell their stories. You'll laugh at some and may shed a few tears at others. We hope each one brings a smile as you recognize the universal qualities that unite us. Being together, being there for the people we care about—what could be a better reason to bake a cake?

So put on the coffee pot or teakettle, cut yourself a generous slice of Collin Street Bakery fruitcake, and get ready to enjoy some of our favorite customer stories.

Bob McNutt
Chairman and President
COLLIN STREET BAKERY

TEXAS DIPLOMACY

Joe Lake is from East Texas, not far from Corsicana, but this fifth-generation Texan had to go to Munich before he got his first taste of Collin Street Bakery fruitcake. Or at least, his first memory of it.

He was 11 years old, it was the early 1950s, and his father had volunteered to serve as an Army dentist in what was still an American- and Soviet-occupied Germany. The pastor of a church in Corsicana had sent the fruitcake to Joe's parents. (The pastor's daughter would later marry Joe's brother.)

"I remember that Corsicana fruitcake box," says Joe. "When you're living overseas, things American stand out. Especially things from Texas—they pulled at the heart strings."

Joe's three years in Germany gave him a lifelong taste for both Collin Street Bakery fruitcake and a career in the Foreign Service. His odyssey as a diplomat in the U.S. Department of State took him to East Asia for ten years, West Africa for six, the Balkans for five, and Washington, D.C., for fourteen—"for my sins," he jokes.

He began in 1962 under Dean Rusk—those "heady and exciting Kennedy years," as he describes them. By 1977, he and his family were in Nigeria. Working for Washington in an isolated place like Nigeria was, says Joe, "the wrong end of the 15,000-mile screwdriver." Few things were easily attainable there, so his family would order meat from the United States once a year and canned food two months ahead.

The Corsicana fruitcake in its familiar tin was a Christmas staple, even in equatorial Lagos, and eventually enjoyed the same VIP delivery method as classified government documents: via diplomatic pouch.

That first year, though, some friends from California mailed Joe and his family their Collin Street Bakery fruitcake. It arrived in the main post office about the same time the entire building went up in flames. There would be no fruitcake for the Lakes that Christmas.

Two years later they were in Kaduna, in northern Nigeria, and received a package—or at least, a semblance of one. The packing box looked as if it had been run through a Bunsen burner and then dunked in a pail of water, and it had taken on a curious round shape—the shape of a tin, like the kind a Collin Street Bakery fruitcake came in.

It was the very same fruitcake that had been through the fire, decidedly dry but revived by the liberal soaking in rum Joe's wife gave it. "It was excellent," says Joe. "Our kids said it was one of the best they had."

Years earlier, when Joe had proposed to his wife, he had cautioned her about what a life in the Foreign Service would mean. Half-jokingly he'd said to her, "If you are okay living in Ouagadougou or Ulaanbaatar, we'll be fine."

By 1990, Joe and his wife were living in Ulaanbaatar.

The city is the capital of Mongolia. "It wasn't the end of the earth but you could see it from there," quips Joe. "If Tibet is the roof of the world, Mongolia is the eaves. It's the second largest landlocked country, with China on one side and Russia on the other. Politically, it was a tough neighborhood."

Joe was the seventh American to live there since 1921, when the newly established Mongolian communist government had expelled all foreigners. The other six were fellow Embassy personnel. The entire country was sparsely populated—just a little over 2.5 million people in a landmass three-fourths the size of the United States.

"Gold would literally wash out of the mountains and there would be no one there to pick it up," says Joe. He and his wife relied on couriers from Beijing, approximately 1500 miles away, to come with fresh food—and the Christmas fruitcake.

"The fruitcake was a real delight," says Joe. "It was fully Texan and truly American." At the time of year it arrived, the temperature hovered around 40 below—Fahrenheit or Celsius, it makes no difference. At that temperature, they're both the same number.

Despite the cold and the isolation, it was an exciting time to be at the end of the earth. Something hot was happening. After seven decades of communist rule, Mongolia was becoming a democracy.

"Democracy has to take root in its own indigenous form to work successfully," Joe says. "The Mongolians had long held some democratic traditions. They were very much a frontier culture, with a strong sense of individualism.

"About forty percent of Mongolians then were nomads who raised camels, sheep, horses, goats, and cattle," he adds. "They related to Americans, and to Texans in particular."

And so, in democratic fashion and with that special brand of hospitality Texans are famous for, Joe shared his Corsicana fruitcake with some of the architects of Mongolian democracy.

Joe semi-retired from the diplomatic service in 1997. After too many years of (diplomatically) eating tough mutton in countries where it was a mainstay, he never goes near it now.

"But we still eat fruitcake. I would add: the only kind we eat is Corsicana fruitcake," he says. "For many years, it was the way my family stayed connected to Texas and the United States."

Besides, it sure tastes good soaked in rum.

CAJUN FRUITCAKE

Michelle Watson was a sheltered young woman from a small Texas town when she married her high school sweetheart, Richard, in 1980 and went to meet his grandparents. She had grown up in Wichita Falls, on the Texas-Oklahoma border, and although Richard's grandparents didn't live that far away, to Michelle it might just as well have been another country. They lived in Jefferson Parish, Louisiana, deep in bayou country.

It was not far from New Orleans, where the young couple went for their honeymoon. That's when Michelle first encountered Dutch, Richard's grandfather, who wasn't Dutch at all but Cajun.

"He had that real thick French accent and would call me 'cher,' and for the longest time I wondered what he was saying," recalls Michelle with a laugh. "I had never been exposed to that culture before, and it was hard for me to understand him. Of course," she adds, "he probably had a hard time with my Texas accent."

Dutch (whose real name was Adam) had worked in one of the shipyards. Despite being a diminutive figure in his early seventies when Michelle met him, he was not a person to be dismissed lightly.

"At first he intimidated me," Michelle confesses. Especially since her husband was one of Dutch's favorite grandchildren. "Dutch was concerned my husband would starve to death because I didn't know Cajun cooking," explains Michelle, laughing. "He'd say to my mother-in-law, 'Poor Ricky—Michelle can't make a roux.'"

I'll bet you can't make enchiladas, Michelle recalls thinking.

Dutch was right: Michelle didn't know how to make a roux, a base used for much Cajun cooking. "It's a thickener for dishes like gumbo," explains Michelle. "You brown flour and oil to a particular color. I considered it a gravy, though Dutch would probably have been insulted if I called it that."

Roux aside, it was food that quickly broke the ice between Dutch and his new granddaughter-in-law. "I soon learned to appreciate the finer points of Cajun cuisine," says Michelle. She especially loved the seafood jambalaya and crawfish étouffée that Richard's grandmother made. She would go with Richard's grandparents deep into the bayou, in Dutch's boat, where she learned how to catch crabs and later cook them.

Michelle had another culinary skill. Being Texan, she knew how to order a Collin Street Bakery fruitcake. "I decided to show Dutch some of the finer aspects of Texas cuisine," she says.

All worries of roux went by the wayside the first Christmas Michelle had a DeLuxe Fruitcake delivered to Dutch. "You can keep sending those fruitcakes," Dutch advised her. "I'd certainly take another one."

Just as Dutch was Michelle's introduction to Cajun culture, she was his introduction to a famous taste of Texas. A new family tradition had begun, and it flourished.

The fruitcake became their unspoken bond—he with his gumbo-thick Cajun accent, she with her Texas lilt—a conversation between just the two of them that needed no words. They now understood and appreciated each other immensely. When he called her *cher*, Michelle now knew it was a term of affection ("dear"), and so could laugh when Dutch informed her that her American-blend coffee "tasted like rabbit pee." He wanted only the traditional Cajun chicory coffee.

But the fruitcake needed no improvement. If anything, it was a little *too* good.

"My mother-in-law told me Dutch would hide the Collin Street Bakery fruitcake when company was coming," says Michelle. "He'd put a real cheap fruitcake into the Collin Street tin. That way he could save the good stuff for himself."

Dutch has since passed away, but Michelle still sends a Corsicana fruitcake to Jefferson Parish, for her father-in-law. Like father, like son—he also hides it to keep for himself, Michelle reports—"although he doesn't substitute a cheap one," she adds.

Michelle, meanwhile, still doesn't know how to make a roux (but her husband hasn't starved to death). When she cuts into her own family's fruitcake, she thinks of Dutch. "Food is such a part of that culture," says Michelle. "Dutch savored that fruitcake. That was his treat and his alone. It was one of the ways he savored life."

THE 196TH COUNTRY

A small world it may be, but there are still places that come as a surprise on the map. Benin, for instance.

Collin Street Bakery fruitcakes have found their way to 196 countries. Up until November 7, 1996, though, the tally was one country shy. That was the day the Bakery shipped an Original DeLuxe Fruitcake to a Peace Corps volunteer named Christopher Robbins. He was working in Toukountouna, Benin.

Being an artist, the one-time University of Virginia student had drawn a map of where Benin was when he posted his plea for a fruitcake. *Afrique de L'Ouest*, his return address read: the West African coast.

Christopher had joined the Peace Corps in 1995. He had been studying at a Japanese university the year before and had taken a trip to Thailand, where he came upon a public campground that Peace Corps volunteers had created from an island prison.

"I was amazed that jobs like that existed," says Christopher, who now lives with his wife in Serbia. He decided then and there to join the Peace Corps, and he knew quite clearly what he could contribute: "the ability to work with limited and constantly changing resources, a creative approach to problem-solving, an open mind to alternative perspectives, a hard work ethic, and an acceptance of the fact that the value systems I grew up with are not absolute or internationally applicable."

What he wasn't so clear about was where he was going to end up. He knew he wanted to work in Africa. "Beyond that," he says, "I had an outdated atlas and a limited sense of geography." (This was before the days of Google Earth and MapQuest.) Peace Corps officials gave him a choice between the Central African Republic and Benin.

When he consulted his atlas, he found the Central African Republic described as the *Empire* of Central Africa. *I don't want to live in an empire*, he recalls thinking. Plus, the country was landlocked. "Benin seemed to have a coastline, so I figured if things got really bad there, at least I could escape to the beach," he says.

Besides, the University of Virginia had curated a show of Benin Bronzes, so this was surely a sign, right? (Except, as Christopher later discovered, that was a different Benin—Benin City, in Nigeria.)

But never mind that it was this little-known country. Christopher quickly fell in love with his work, the people he was serving, and Benin. So much so that he got a deed to a small scrap of land and built his home there, by hand, fashioning mud and straw and sticks into an artful hut.

It was all he needed, but it lacked, as he says, a homey touch.

One day, on one of his two-hour cycling trips to the largest nearby town, Natitingou, Christopher called in at the office of a fellow volunteer and spied a Collin Street Bakery catalog. How did such mail find its way all the way from Corsicana, Texas, to Natitingou, Benin, Christopher wanted to know. My mother sent it, was the reply.

Christopher decided then and there that he wanted one, too. "It just seemed like it would be a very homey thing, to come back to my mud hut and find an unexpected catalog of fruitcake," he says.

Even though he was never homesick in Benin, somehow having this "comforting thing" of a fruitcake catalog made it all the better. And even though the Bakery staff dispatched not only the catalog but the fruitcake, what was perhaps most important was that Christopher had, in a manner of speaking, put Benin on the map.

Benin turned out to be the better choice of countries for another reason, and it had nothing to do with the beach. While Christopher was there he met a Peace Corps volunteer named Shelly, who was serving in a village about four bicycle hours from Christopher's. He was used to biking the two hours to Natitingou, but "after I met her, I decided I needed the extra two hours of exercise," he says.

Shelly is now his wife.

MOTHER-AND-DAUGHTER REUNION

Lynn Lastrapes raised three boys and took care of many more children as a schoolteacher. But for a few "stolen quiet moments" before Christmas every year, she became the child again, the daughter whom her mother doted on, as she did all three of her girls.

It wasn't that her mother showered them with expensive presents. It was simpler than that. "My mother was very good at doing the little things that mean so much," says Lynn.

When Lynn and her husband would travel from their home in Baton Rouge to Philadelphia to visit their youngest son at college, her mother would leave her home in New Orleans to come babysit. The Lastrapes' children were grown, but their little Yorkshire terrier wasn't, and could not be left alone. "Mother understood that," says Lynn. "She would do these things that would put her out, and she did them in such a loving way."

As a child, Lynn was given piano lessons. Her mother finally took up the piano at age 72; she had always wanted to play. She and Lynn sometimes practiced together.

But it was the fruitcake Lynn loved most. Not only the taste but the constancy of it. Every year, the week before Christmas, her mother would send it to her. "I had permission to open it the week before," Lynn recalls. "She understood how hectic my life was and would say, 'This will help you get through the holidays.'"

It became one of their special little rituals, a tradition Lynn knew would be repeated again and again every year, like the notes on the piano her mother would practice.

"I never bothered to interest my husband or children in discovering a taste for it," says Lynn, trying to sound sheepish. "It was the only thing too precious to share with my loved ones. Besides," she adds with a laugh, "I had three big boys. That fruitcake would have been gone in a morning!"

And so Lynn would steal over to "the little tin" of Collin Street Bakery fruitcake, which she kept "kind of out of sight," and have herself a sliver with a cup of tea, and enjoy those few stolen quiet moments of delicious solitude. Except that she didn't feel alone; it was as if her mother were there.

Lynn's mother died in 2002 at age 91. When the week before Christmas came that year, the Collin Street Bakery fruitcake didn't. Lynn couldn't bring herself to order one because she remembered: she remembered the constancy we seek as children and continue to cherish even after childhood is lost. She remembered her mother.

A couple of years ago, Lynn and her family took care of an out-of-town friend who had come to Baton Rouge to have some surgery. As a thank-you gift, he sent Lynn a Collin Street Bakery fruitcake. "One of the great big ones," she adds. "It must have weighed fifty pounds."

No little tin this time that could be tucked away. Nor did Lynn want it to be. "This time," she says, "I shared."

That was when she understood that, even though her mother was gone, this was a way of being with her again. "I now realize that, instead of sadness, my mother would love to see me enjoying that Collin Street fruitcake and remembering a very special part of our love for each other."

The friend who sent the fruitcake hadn't heard about the tradition, and he unknowingly started a new one. Now at Christmas every year, Lynn has a few stolen, precious moments of reunion with her mother.

THE ETERNAL FRUITCAKE

Steven Bloom's father started the Collin Street Bakery fruitcake tradition for Steven and his brother when the two were college students more than thirty years ago. The brothers, starved for something that tasted delicious and not institutional, pounced on their respective cakes the minute the packages arrived. Knowing their roommates would do the same given the chance, they had to find some impregnable hiding places for the fruitcakes in between gobblings. "I'd like to think the need to find a secure hiding place to sequester the fruitcake was partly attributable to my missing so many classes," says Steven.

His father continued the tradition when Steven graduated, married, and moved to New York City with his family. Over the years, says Steven, "as I dealt with life's ever-changing dynamics, several constants remained in my life: weekly telephone calls to my family, going home to upstate New York for the holidays, summer vacations, and the eagerly anticipated, annual Collin Street Bakery fruitcake."

But in 1988, Steven's work took him to Rome, and he figured that would be the end of finding the familiar red tin in the mail, courtesy of his father. Italy was half a world away, FedEx International was in its infancy, and the Roman lifestyle was a whole other world from the get-it-done-now pace of New York City. "I felt fortunate to have the opportunity to live and work in the Eternal City," says Steven. "But there were times when the slow pace of life in Rome could become frustrating. I occasionally suggested that the sobriquet 'Eternal City' had been bequeathed to Rome because it took so long to get things done."

Like getting the mail.

Sending mail from the U.S. to Rome in those days was not for the faint of heart. Rome often functioned in spite of its institutions, rather than because of them, the postal system being no exception. In the days before faxes and e-mails, some U.S. organizations were even known to send their important correspondence to Rome via diplomatic pouch, so uncertain were the mail deliveries.

So by the time the little yellow slip appeared in the Blooms' mailbox one hot day in July the following year, announcing that a parcel was waiting for them at the post office, Steven barely missed a beat. He simply wasn't expecting anything. But he went down to the local post office branch anyway, only to be told the package had been sent to the central post office in Rome.

Steven weighed the situation: a 45-minute trip, in a non-air-conditioned bus, in 90-degree heat, to a bad neighborhood. He considered chucking the idea and the little yellow slip, but then curiosity overcame dread and off he went.

"The central post office in Rome is only slightly smaller than the state of Rhode Island and, arguably, just a bit more organized," Steven jokes. It was a maze of delivery trucks from all over Europe, a mass of loading docks, and a muddle of millions of pieces of mail. He clutched his by-now soggy yellow slip, sweating past dock after dock of mail (the building was also not air conditioned), boggled by the sheer scale of the place. "The space could easily accommodate a Boeing 747 with sufficient room remaining for a three-ring circus," says Steven.

In the midst of this Fellini-esque scene, he came across a group of postal workers playing cards. Steven handed one of them the soggy yellow wad that was once a delivery slip and watched incredulously as the man took stock of the million or so pieces of mail, headed for a shelf, pulled down a package, and placed in Steven's hand the package from his father containing the Collin Street Bakery fruitcake, now eight months old.

Steven's shock of delight in getting his 1988 Christmas fruitcake played itself out again when he rushed it home (well, rushed by Roman standards) and opened the tin. "It tasted just fine," he says.

And so it is that in the Eternal City, hopes of getting the mail can spring eternal. The chain of a cherished tradition Steven's father had begun in a dorm room and continued through a lifetime remained unbroken. Sometimes you just have to wait a little longer for the next link to appear.

AMERICAN VALENTINE

Rudolf Scheffrahn knew an order when he heard one—he'd served in the army, after all. So whenever his wife, Lia, reminded him that they were to stop at Collin Street Bakery on their way from Boerne to Mineola or Tyler to visit family and friends, he knew she meant business.

And remind him she did, for twenty-five years. "It was a consistent cookie stop in Corsicana," as Rudolf describes it, "three or four times a year."

Occasionally Rudolf would suggest they skip the cookies. "It did not work," he reports with a laugh. "She insisted, and that was an order. If ever there were a totally devoted Collin Street Bakery customer, it was she," adds Rudolf, who celebrated his ninetieth birthday on May 20, 2008.

And if ever there were a totally devoted husband, it was he.

Rudolf and Lia's story is a love story of a special generation, a story of devotion to one another and to one's country—not because you were born an American, but because you wanted to be an American.

They were post-war immigrants, among the 1,350 German immigrants who sailed past the Statue of Liberty along with their first-born son on June 10, 1952, aboard the U.S. troop transport *General C.C. Ballow*. Lia was 27, her husband 33. They were leaving Germany to escape the hunger and other harsh conditions of the time. But they were coming to America for something more.

"We came to America with hope for a better life," says Rudolf.

He was a master watch- and clockmaker, practicing his craft in Indiana and California before retiring in Texas. Lia was a homemaker, raising their children and planning for their future. "It was always my dear wife who said the education of our sons was most important," recalls Rudolf. "She was saving every penny for a college education for her two boys."

He credits his wife's frugality for why both sons graduated from college with no student loans to pay. The older one is now a dentist, the younger one a university professor.

Lia and Rudolf had come to America for a better life and had found it. As soon as the law allowed, they and their German-born son pledged their allegiance to their new country. On February 14, 1958—Valentine's Day—the Scheffrahns became proud American citizens.

Reflecting on that day a half century later, Rudolf says: "It's the most wonderful experience a person can have. You are so grateful having a new homeland, America!"

Lia and Rudolf voted in every election since 1958—"never missed it," as he says. For Lia, that last election came in 2006. She passed away on February 27, 2007.

But not in spirit.

Two months later, the Texas House of Representatives passed a resolution in recognition of Lia's "courage, resourcefulness, and love," and flew the Texas flag over the State Capitol in her honor.

Valentine's Day 2008 would have marked Lia's golden anniversary as a U.S. citizen. And so Rudolf, together with his older son and his wife, celebrated the occasion at a restaurant in Tyler, a photograph of Lia at the table.

There is another way that Lia lives on: Rudolf continues to make his Corsicana cookie stops. He knows that's an order.

And he knows something else, too.

Says Rudolf, "After coming to America, our life was wonderful."

PARABOLIC FRUITCAKE

Jacquelyn Kilgo was forever looking for problems—math problems, that is, for the students in her high school algebra class. Which is why the ad in the magazine for Collin Street Bakery's Classic Christmas Cake had caught her eye.

"I wanted to show the kids that math problems weren't just in textbooks," says Jacquelyn, who taught at Hubbard High School, just about twenty-five miles from Corsicana and Collin Street. "I wanted them to think out of the box." And so they did: out of the box, and into the bakery.

"The Classic Christmas Cake," the magazine ad announced. The ad went on to list three sizes of fruitcakes and their (1995) prices:

Regular (1⅞ lbs.)	$15.75
Medium (2⅞ lbs.)	$22.95
Large (4⅞ lbs.)	$37.95

It was a perfect problem for Jacquelyn's students, who were using their Texas Instruments graphing calculators that had just come into vogue. "The beauty of the TI calculators was that the machines did the math but the students did the problem-solving," says Jacquelyn.

The two sets of numbers—the weights of the fruitcakes and the prices for each—provided ideal points to plot on a graph. "Was this a quadratic, linear, or cubic function? I wanted the students to see the answer on the graph," says Jacquelyn.

Having drawn a graph of the information, the students then had to answer some questions:

✳ What was the equation for the graph?

✳ What was the slope?

✳ What was the real-world significance for the slope?

✳ What was the y-intercept?

✳ What was the real-world significance for the y-intercept?

And then:

✳ How much would a 3½-pound fruitcake cost?

What the students (along with their teacher) soon realized was that it wasn't the straight-line equation they'd thought it would be, but rather, a parabolic function. (Translation for those who need a refresher course in algebra: it curved.)

About thirty students were in Jacquelyn's two math classes, and most of them got the problem right. "I was hoping the advanced ones would solve the regression equation, and they did," she says.

Jacquelyn was a teacher for thirty-one years. (She retired in 2001.) She started off in elementary education but, dismayed by how her own children learned math in high school, went back to school to become a math teacher. She was determined to make math challenging but enjoyable for her students.

A fruitcake equation did just that—especially when the kids received a complimentary DeLuxe Fruitcake from Collin Street Bakery as thanks for their applied mathematics.

Jacquelyn had another reason for choosing a fruitcake: it was Christmastime when she assigned the problem, and she figured the kids would be thinking about traditional holiday foods.

As would she.

As a child growing up in Hubbard, Jacquelyn grew up on Collin Street Bakery fruitcakes. Her grandparents lived there, too, and every Christmas it would be there at her grandparents' open house: her grandmother's homemade eggnog and the Collin Street Bakery fruitcake.

"From the time I was 3 years old I remember that," says Jacquelyn. "I can just see that fruitcake tin in my grandmother's dining room."

Today she still remembers those Christmases: she inherited her grandmother's dining room furniture, the very furniture where the bowl of eggnog and the tin of fruitcake would be. Every time she dusts the table, it serves as a touchstone of family and holiday memories.

One of Jacquelyn's greatest joys is bumping into her former math students and having them tell her she'll never guess, but they're now teaching high school math.

"When you're a teacher, a little bit of you gets passed on to the next generations," says Jacquelyn of the career she loved.

And perhaps, a little bit of fruitcake math as well.

⸺⟫•⟪⸺

Grade your paper

Did you take Mrs. Kilgo's math test?

More than twelve years after she gave her kids the "fruitcake test," Jacquelyn worked out the answers herself ("fortunately, I still had my graphing calculator"). Here they are, and with this caution: remember that these were 1995 prices. It's always good to check your math.

The Classic Christmas Cake	
Regular (1⅞ lbs.)	$15.75
Medium (2⅞ lbs.)	$22.95
Large (4⅞ lbs.)	$37.95

* What is the equation for the graph?

    Linear: $y = 7.34x + 2.32$

    Quadratic: $y = -0.3899x^2 + 10.03x - 1.689$

* What is the slope?

    Linear: 7.34

    Quadratic: *no slope*

* What is the real-world significance for the slope?

    Cost per pound

* What is the y-intercept?

    2.32

* What is the real-world significance for the y-intercept?

    Fixed cost before weight is considered

* How much would a 3½-pound fruitcake cost?

    Using a linear function: *$28.01*

    Using a quadratic function: *$28.64*

Here is the graph, which Jacquelyn cautions is graphed as a linear function rather than quadratic:

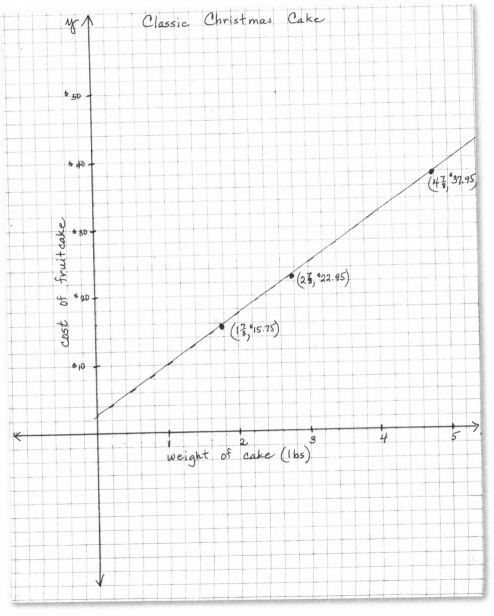

MEMORIES IN THE MAKING

Imagine not liking your grandma's baking. For Victoria Wendt, that was the fact of the matter when it came to her grandmother's homemade fruitcake. But when her father's mother took to ordering a Collin Street Bakery DeLuxe Fruitcake instead, "one taste and I was hooked," says Victoria.

Her father, Owen, continued the tradition after her grandmother passed away. But Victoria's family members, who live in Newport, Oregon, were not content merely with the tried-and-true. (Perhaps it's a vestige of the pioneering spirit of other, earlier Oregon families.) They ventured into the apricot fruitcake, a favorite of Victoria's.

Then, emboldened by how popular the cakes were with his family, in 2008 Owen Wendt added a newcomer to the Collin Street Christmas list: blueberry cheesecake.

And that's when all hell broke loose. The Wendt family's cheesecake wars had begun. Victoria explains:

"Half the family liked to eat their cheesecake half-frozen so the blueberries crackled in their mouth, the other half liked the cheesecake completely thawed and refrigerated so the whole bite melted in their mouth."

Happily, this was a war both sides could win and still save face (as well as dessert). "We kept the majority of the cheesecake frozen, and the piece we took off to eat, we would let thaw. Those who liked it half-frozen ate their cheesecake early, those who liked it completely thawed had theirs later," says Victoria.

But for Victoria's father, the Christmas of the cheesecake wars was also one when he was fighting a much more serious battle. He had contracted colon cancer. The Collin Street Bakery fruitcakes were among the few foods that didn't upset his stomach. "They were packed with enough calories that he was able to survive on them for a while," says Victoria. "We always made sure he had enough fruitcake left so he was able to eat with us during regular meals."

Owen Wendt passed away a month after Christmas. His daughter has taken up his tradition of indulging the family at holiday time with Collin Street Bakery fruitcakes (and cheesecakes). "It's a good way to remember both my grandma and my dad," says Victoria. "We hold it as a mini-celebration of their lives."

SHEEPHERDER'S STEW

The only hint of Bob Snead's time in Vietnam is in the subject matter of much of his art these days: soldiers.

Bob has always been an artist, even before he was a soldier, and now that he's retired from thirty years in the military, he's able to pursue his passion for painting full time. He has a series of paintings on the Buffalo Soldiers—African Americans who served in the U.S. Army since Civil War days and during America's westward expansion. The series features more than 165 canvases, fourteen limited-edition prints, and a painting that became the model for the Buffalo Soldier statue at Fort Bliss.

"I've always been involved in the arts," says Bob, who settled in El Paso with his family after his many tours of duty. "It's like being in athletics—you take advantage of opportunities."

For Bob that meant practicing his craft even while he was perfecting his salute. In the Army he became the jack-of-all-artistic-trades—draftsman, poster maker, illustrator, and cartoonist for the Army Times Publishing Company.

"I was in the 82nd Airborne Division, where we had a publication called STRAC Facts. STRAC was an acronym for Skilled, Tough, Ready Around the Clock," says Bob, adding with a laugh, "but of course, being soldiers, we changed it and made it Stupid Troopers Running Around in Circles."

One of his well-known comic strip characters was Rip Riser, a fellow paratrooper. Rip is retired Army now, but Bob remains as busy as ever with his art. In February 2004, the Governor appointed him to the Texas Commission on the Arts.

Bill McNutt, one of the owners of Collin Street Bakery, was also serving on the Commission. When the two met, and Bill mentioned the name Collin Street Bakery, all a startled but delighted Bob Snead could say was: "You're kidding."

Chief Warrant Officer 4 Robert Snead of the 52nd Combat Aviation Battalion returned from his four tours of duty in Vietnam with two Purple Hearts, two Bronze Stars, three Vietnam Cross of Gallantry medals, and forty-one air medals.

But what he cherishes even more than medals is the memory of that Thanksgiving Eve dinner in 1967.

It was Bob's first tour of duty in 'Nam. There would be three more—in 1970,

1971, and 1973—and his helicopter would be shot down, but that Wednesday in November of '67 was a good day. Not just because the weather was pleasant there in Pleiku, north of Saigon in the Central Highlands—not hot, a little brisk in fact, but not yet into the rainy season. There was another reason.

"There were about twenty or thirty pilots in my unit," says Bob. "We'd all gone out that day and had all been involved in some kind of hostile activity. But no one got shot."

That's what made it such a good day.

To celebrate, they decided they'd make their specialty: sheepherder's stew.

"I don't remember who coined the phrase sheepherder's stew," says Bob. "It might have been my buddy Al. It was basically a conglomeration of what everybody had in their hooch."

Outside their hooch, or living quarters, the group had dug a big barbecue pit. Into it they placed the ten-gallon cook pot they'd permanently borrowed from the mess hall and started mixing the fixings. The basic recipe was roughly four or five cans of corned beef, pork and beans, onions, hot sauce, and whatever else looked good.

But this time, the meal didn't stop with the stew. This was Thanksgiving Eve, after all. "Somebody had a bottle of brandy," says Bob. "And one of the men from Texas had fruitcakes—a lot of fruitcakes from a place called Collin Street Bakery."

It was a feast. And the kind of impromptu celebratory meal that leads to something more: to a spontaneity that will never be quite as good ever again.

"Somebody would start off a song from home—like *Swanee River*—and we'd all start singing," says Bob. "It sent a chill up your spine. There was such camaraderie and closeness," he adds. "If you've never been there, you don't know what it means."

It is a moment Bob has long carried in his heart. More than thirty-five years later, when he heard Bill McNutt say "Collin Street Bakery" at the Texas Commission on the Arts gathering, "it brought back good memories," he says.

Over the years, Bob has maintained the friendships with his fellow sheepherder-stew soldiers, all members of the First Aviation Brigade. They shared something only they can fully appreciate.

"Those were good days," says Bob. "There is no place I ever would have wanted to be except with those guys."

A MATTER OF TRUST

For Doris and Steve's two grown children, Christmas has always meant what it has for many: Collin Street Bakery fruitcake. But for Jenny and Greg, that association led to another equally wonderful connection. Christmas meant fruitcake, fruitcake meant their beloved Grandma and Grandpa.

"My kids always associated fruitcake with their grandparents," says Doris. "No matter where we lived, my mom and dad would send us that Texas fruitcake for Christmas."

Steve was a Navy pilot, so over the years the fruitcake ended up on doorsteps far from Doris's parents' home in St. Louis—Rhode Island, Maryland, California, Florida, Japan. Her parents were continuing a tradition they had begun when Doris was a little girl.

"My parents were offspring of diligent German farmers in the Midwest who worked hard every day and saved their pennies," says Doris. "For my folks, that fruitcake was a luxury."

But for Christmas, that didn't matter. There was always a Collin Street Bakery fruitcake under Doris's childhood tree.

"We couldn't open the fruitcake till Christmas morning," Doris says. The one exception (rather reluctantly executed) was if aunts and uncles came for dinner before Christmas Day. Even when Doris went to her grandparents' for Christmas Eve festivities, the fruitcake remained safely ensconced under the tree at home. It was the last thing Doris opened—and then it got devoured.

"Sometimes it would make it to the day after Christmas, but not always," Doris says with a laugh. Her mother put the empty tins to use, some of them holding her needles and threads.

And so this delicious bit of indulgence for the frugal Germans continued when they had their grandchildren. It became one of the threads that held them together, even when they were physically far apart, even when both kids were grown up and had houses of their own.

Greg and Jenny lost their grandfather first, in 1997. In October 2004, their grandmother passed away. As Doris was working on her mother's estate, she quickly discovered that her cautious parents who had saved their pennies had left trusts to both of her children.

How best to tell them? Doris wondered.

In her mother's recent stack of mail was the Collin Street Bakery catalog. That's when Doris knew how she would tell Greg and Jenny about their inheritance.

The trust officer on the twelfth floor of the plush bank office in St. Louis could only stare as Doris instructed him on how she wanted the bank to notify her children. They were not to simply make a phone call.

"I wanted something my kids would instantly equate with their Grandma and Grandpa," says Doris, "something that could be mailed."

In short order, two small Collin Street Bakery fruitcakes were delivered to the twelfth floor of the plush bank office.

"I opened the boxes, put the trust papers inside, and had the bank put on the form, 'From Grandma and Grandpa'," says Doris.

Greg and Jenny were allowed to open the boxes when they arrived. But, says Doris, "we all still wait until Christmas morning before we have our fruitcake."

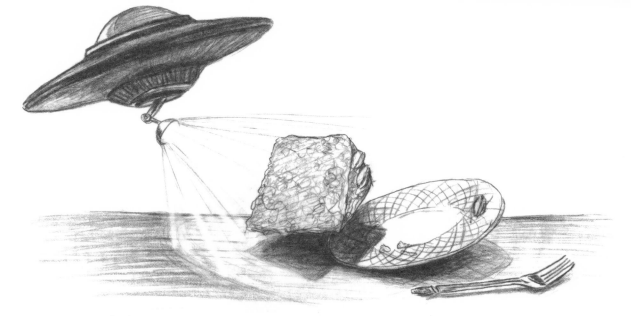

'E.T., PHONE HOME—AND BRING THE FRUITCAKE'

We've often had the pleasure of having customers tell us our fruitcake is out of this world. It wasn't until we heard from one customer in particular, however, that we realized just how true this statement might be.

Here is the correspondence Joe Waters, a longtime customer, sent us:

I have longed to tell this story for years. I attempted it once but no one would believe it. Please forgive me if I am a little confused about the dates, but ever since the abduction I have had a problem with time.

This is the story no one believes.

Many years ago I was traveling through the area around Roswell, New Mexico. It was about Christmastime. I was a little down on my luck, but fortunately a friend had sent me several Collin Street Bakery fruitcakes and other items.

As luck would have it my old mini-bus broke down in the middle of the night. I was stranded on a back road miles from nowhere. Well, there was nothing else to do, so I took out an aluminum blanket, and prepared for a nap until help might come.

No sooner had I closed my eyes than a light came from out of the sky and focused itself on my blanket. Immediately it became hot. I got up and retreated to the mini-bus. Before I knew it, the bus and I were lifted up in a swirling tornado of light. We came to rest in a white room that glowed with a ghostly orange-ish white light. The next thing I knew I was communicating with strange-looking beings. They all looked weird—sort of burnt orange—and they had long horn-like appendages sticking out of their heads.

I was glad they caught me later. They said if I were sooner they would have eliminated me. When they saw the address on my package was Corsicana, Texas, they became less inclined toward violence. I offered them a piece of fruitcake. After they tasted it, they agreed to let me go if I turned over all my Collin Street goodies. They said they had to take samples of the best Earth had to offer back to planet t u.

Then they put me back into my mini-bus and dropped me on a hill near Roswell. Unfortunately the bus was traveling so fast at the time they released it, it smashed into the mayor's bedroom. The sheriff did not believe my story because I did not have any fruitcake left. As a matter of fact, the judge tried to draw an analogy between me and your excellent product.

In all humility, there is no comparison.

This story is true. How else can anyone explain the frequent sightings of extra-terrestrial objects near Roswell, New Mexico, since then?

I don't understand why they just don't go to Corsicana. Maybe their burnt-orange color and the things growing out of their heads distort their sense of direction. Or could be they think there is an insufficient supply of tea in Corsicana. Well, even though their sense of direction may be questionable, even t u-vians know good fruitcake when they eat it.

Now, you may be asking yourself, is this just a giant spoof? Well, it's a big world out there—and up there—so who knows? But we do know Joe's last known earthly address was Bryan, Texas, which is where we've been sending his fruitcakes. Where they land after that—well, the heavens only know.

LOVE AT FIRST SLICE

When Mary Lou McKie turned down the invitation to go sailing that warm February day in Miami Beach back in 1967, she didn't think twice about it. After all, she'd never even met the gentleman who had invited her. But he proved to be persistent—to say nothing of charming—and in true Prince Charming fairy-tale style, they would soon be sailing happily off into the sunset together.

The gentleman's name was Cornelius Vanderbilt Jr. Yes, *that* Vanderbilt—he was the great-great-grandson and namesake of "The Commodore," as the first Cornelius Vanderbilt liked to be called, the nineteenth-century business titan who made his fortune in steamships and the railroad.

Mary Lou just called his descendant Neil.

It turns out that Cornelius Vanderbilt Jr. had been a longtime customer of Collin Street Bakery. He lived in Miami Beach in the 1960s, not far from where Mary Lou was living and where Bill and Josephine McNutt wintered. As the owners of Collin Street Bakery, the McNutts always enjoyed meeting their customers, so they'd arranged to meet up with Neil in Miami that February. Mary Lou's sister and brother-in-law, friends of the McNutts from back home in Corsicana, were visiting at the time. One of them mentioned Mary Lou to Neil, who suggested she join them.

"He wasn't looking for a date. He was just being gracious and inviting me to come along," says Mary Lou. But she was in the throes of a divorce, with three young daughters to care for, and a job to answer to, and didn't feel she should go.

Well then, they would have to do dinner, Neil told Mary Lou's sister.

And that will be that, Mary Lou thought. "I hardly expected him to remember extending a dinner invitation, but he did."

It was pretty much love at first sight.

"We had this instant rapport," says Mary Lou. "We started talking and time just got away from us. We almost missed dinner. I felt like Cinderella," she says, laughing, "and I kept looking around for the pumpkin."

There was no midnight pumpkin, but by the next morning, two things happened: roses arrived from her Prince Charming, and she was catapulted into the society section of the newspaper.

"His name was magical," says Mary Lou. "If I had been younger at the time, I might have thought I was something special."

As far as Neil was concerned, she was. For their second date, he brought presents for each of her daughters. When Mary Lou went to Corsicana to visit her sister in May, he came to see her. And when she decided to move back home to Texas that August, after her father died, Neil told her: "Then find a house for me, because I'm coming, too."

They were married November 4, 1967.

But while it was a romance, all was not a fairy tale. "The day before we were to be married, Neil had a stroke," Mary Lou says. "The doctor didn't think he would live a year."

The stroke left him with aphasia. Since Neil was a writer, with nearly three dozen books to his credit, losing his facility with the language was a blow. But Mary Lou says he was not one to give up—or slow down.

"He was older than I, but I was the stodgy one," she says with a laugh. He proved his doctor wrong, living far past the year they had given him, until 1974. "It was a perfect time in his life and mine," says Mary Lou. "He was wonderful to my children and me."

And to his friends. Neil sent many gifts of Collin Street Bakery fruitcakes over the years. Mary Lou still does. After all, as she says, "It was indirectly through this fruitcake that I met and married Cornelius Vanderbilt Jr."

THE FORTY-YEAR REUNION

After forty years or so, even the best memories of high school can start to fade. But for Victoria Amos (who was then Victoria Richards), one of her memories of Clermont Northeastern High School in Owensville, Ohio, was so enduring, she could literally taste it. Her older brother, who played trumpet in the high school band, sold Collin Street Bakery fruitcakes as part of a fundraising effort for the band.

"Everybody in my family adored that fruitcake," says Victoria. Her grandmother always bought a couple, and her father would order two or three of the largest size. "My brother made quite a bit of money from those fruitcakes," Victoria recalls with a laugh.

But then her brother graduated and the band stopped the fundraiser and the fruitcakes disappeared—"much to my father's disappointment," Victoria adds.

This was long before Google or the Internet, and so for a family in Ohio who had never placed their order directly, their much-loved fruitcake seemed to vanish into the Texas air.

"For years I tried to make my own fruitcake, but nothing could satisfy us," Victoria says. She tried buying various brands, but that didn't work either. "They were always very dry, a lot more cake than fruit, not like the one I remembered," says Victoria, who now lives in Tennessee. "As my mother has often said, 'I had my mouth fixed' on the Collin Street cake, and nothing else would do." And so for years—decades, actually—Victoria carried with her a memory of what her mouth had been fixed on.

Then, a few years ago Victoria was watching a segment on TV on, of all things, fruitcake. The bakery being featured was located in Texas.

That has to be it, Victoria remembers thinking. "The appearance of the cake was exactly as I remembered it. And we ate enough of them that I would remember." This time around, Victoria had the advantage of an Internet that could virtually take her to the Collin Street Bakery.

"The picture on the website was unmistakable," she says. In a flash, she was on the phone to her father. *I think I found it,* she told him. *Order it,* came the swift reply. And it wasn't even Christmas.

After all those years of her mouth being fixed for a certain taste, Victoria would finally get to satisfy that craving…maybe. But would that really hold after such a long time? How many things really taste, smell, feel as good to us as grownups as they did when we were kids? If anyone should know the answer, it's Victoria: she's a psychotherapist. She understands how memory can fool.

"It tasted exactly the same," says Victoria, with something like triumph in her voice.

The more lots of things in life change, the more a few things remain the same. The recipe for the Collin Street Bakery fruitcake is one of them. So while many memories are best left untested, a few will not disappoint when rekindled.

Victoria now orders her high-school-band fruitcake for Christmas, Father's Day, and one other occasion. "We all get together for a family reunion in Tennessee in the summer," she says, "and we all have Texas fruitcake."

Strike up the band—sometimes you can, indeed, go home again.

LABEL HER SENTIMENTAL

For many, it is that first bite of fruitcake that summons the memories of a loved one so vividly, you can taste it. For others it is the tin, a self-made treasure chest for keeping the small objects that loom large in memory. But for Lindsay Shuster, neither of these things became the object of her affection when her father passed away.

Shortly after the autumn day John Lorenzen died, Lindsay received the last of her father's many gifts to her. It was the Collin Street Bakery fruitcake he'd been ordering for her every Christmas, even though Lindsay and her husband had lived in the house next door to his for thirty-five years.

What Lindsay treasures more than anything from that last gift is the mailing label on the shipping package. "I keep it in my special place where I keep special things," she says. "It was important for me to know what he did that last week in his life."

As she soon understood, her father was putting all *his* things, special and ordinary, in order. He was 93 and had just been hospitalized. He came home and, as Lindsay says, knew it was time. That last week he left his daughter detailed lists of what she should do as his executor, returned a recent purchase he wasn't satisfied with to the department store, paid his property taxes—and ordered seven Collin Street Bakery fruitcakes as Christmas gifts for his family and friends.

"My dad was just the greatest person," says Lindsay. "Trust him to give us a surprise when he was gone."

Lindsay had been trying to convince her dad to do his banking online, but he had resisted. Perhaps it was just as well for a daughter who values the small objects of memory.

One of Lindsay's first steps as executor was to see if any bills needed attention. "I pulled out his checkbook to see if we needed to pay anything and said, 'Oh, my goodness'," says Lindsay. There she saw her father's meticulous recording of his last check, number 5668, to Collin Street Bakery, for the fruitcakes. Lindsay now has the canceled check.

"In the last few years of my father's life, I knew there would come a day when it would be the last fruitcake he'd send," says Lindsay. When that fruitcake arrived, as much as she loves it, she couldn't bring herself to cut into it. It's in her freezer, waiting.

How does she think this memory-laden gift will taste, once she finally breaks into it? Says Lindsay: "Bittersweet."

The Cowboy and the Soldier

Even as a kid, Gary Penney wondered what the design on the Collin Street Bakery fruitcake tin meant. "I couldn't figure out why there was snow and a cowboy," Gary says.

He saw enough of those tins as a youngster—Gary is Corsicana born and bred, and his mother worked at the bakery in the 1970s during the busy Christmas season. But he's never wondered about the contents of those tins. "There's a little slice of Texas pride in every piece of that fruitcake," Gary says.

What really matters about the tin, he's decided, is what it means to him.

Gary is a cowboy poet, an avocation he's pursued since 2004. So he knew how he was going to express his feelings about the cowboy and the snow. He even had an idea for how he would finish the poem. The hardest part, he says, was how to begin.

His 5-year-old grandson offered the solution. "My little grandson is just like me when I was a kid," Gary says. "He's curious. When I showed him the tin, he asked me what it meant."

Gary had his beginning.

Shortly after Gary finished the poem, he came to the Collin Street Bakery store in Corsicana and recited it.

"An elderly woman came up to me afterwards and she was crying," Gary says. "She told me her brother had been a POW in World War II. He and the other prisoners were put on a march. At one point her brother spotted this torn piece of paper on the ground and bent down to pick it up. The paper had 'Collin Street Bakery' printed on it."

Seeing this scrap of the familiar helped keep that Texas soldier going, the woman told Gary, and helped get him through the war.

Gary is right: what matters is what the cowboy on the tin means to each person who cherishes its reassuring constancy and familiarity. Here is his poem.

The Cowboy on the Tin
by Gary Penney

One of my little grandsons

Just recently came out for a stay.

He's kinda like his ol' grandpaw,

And he always has somethin' to say.

He likes to dig in my old barns and sheds

Always looking for hidden "treasure."

And he always brings his "finds" to me

'Cause it gives him so much pleasure.

But one day when he came to me,

He had a real puzzled look on his face.

Kinda like a look you'd see

If you saw a ship from outer space.

"Hey Pops," he said,

As he approached me with a puzzled grin.

"I found a bunch of old nails and stuff

In this funny looking beat-up tin."

"I ain't never seen nothing like this

While digging 'round all your old machines.

Can you tell me what I found here?

Can you tell me what this means?"

I knew right away what he'd found

When I caught sight of that old can.

The first time I saw that artwork was many years ago,

Before I ever became a man.

"Carter," I said,

As I looked into his inquisitive little eyes.

"Let's go sit on the porch in our rocking chairs

And I'll tell you about your prize."

A Slice of Life

"This wonderful can came from Corsicana;
A Texas town filled with pride.
The people there make delicious fruitcakes,
That are known by folks worldwide."

"The amazing graphic on this can
Was designed many years ago.
But the artist's name was never signed,
And of him we'll never know."

"So I'll do my best as we look at this lid
To tell of its grand old story.
Not only did this can hold a delicious cake,
But it tells of Texas glory."

"The snow scene with the carriage and house
Tells me this is a long way from here.
Do you see that fine lady and gentleman?
Do you see their gifts of holiday cheer?"

"I'd bet they're on a Christmas visit,

Because they look so happy and jolly.

But what gives the season away to me is

The bow in the berries and holly."

"Giving a fruitcake to your friends

Has become a holiday tradition.

And the Collin Street Bakery in Corsicana

Bakes for that very intention."

"Now I believe that that's the tale

This beautiful snow scene is trying to tell.

This artwork confirms what I told you,

And it does it so very well."

"But Pops!" said Carter,

With a disappointed look on his face.

"Tell me about the cowboy;

Tell me about his space!"

A Slice of Life

"He's right there in the middle of the lid,

Twirling that big ol' rope!

Did you leave him out on purpose?

Are you trying to pull a joke?"

"Settle down Carter."

I said with a sheepish grin.

"I'll tell you about the cowboy,

And now the real story begins."

"You see that old yellow building

Up near the top of the can?

That building is the Alamo,

Where the heartbeat of Texas began."

"One hundred and eighty-five men

Stood so our Republic could be free.

They barricaded themselves against five thousand,

And they did it for you and me."

"For thirteen days of bloody glory
They mustered and fought and died.
Right there in that old Spanish mission was born
Our own inherent Texas pride."

"The battle for Texas independence
Was bought and paid for in that war.
You can see that sign of our freedom and pride
Shining in that bright 'Lone Star.'"

"And right there in the middle of that star
Is another great symbol of our state.
That ol' cowboy represents our grit and spirit,
And what makes our people so great."

"From the top of his hat to the rowels of his spurs,
To the Colt hanging there at his side.
You can tell this old cowboy means business,
And he takes serious his Texas pride."

A Slice of Life

"Men like him helped to build this land

Through courage and sheer determination.

His gutting it out when times were hard

Helped to give us a pride in our nation."

"And that great pride still lives on today,

Down deep in every Texan's heart.

When you tell someone that you're from Texas,

Well, that just kinda sets you apart."

"So now when you see this ol' cowboy on the tin,

I hope you'll think of Texas pride.

And think about this 'secret ingredient'

That was added to the cake inside."

"Well, Carter, that's about it;

I really don't know what else to say.

You've found a pretty cool prize there.

I'd say you've had a pretty good day."

Silently he sat there for a few seconds more

As he pondered the old cowboy's fate.

Then he looked up at me and he smiled and he said,

"I love you Pops."

"I think I'll go see if Grams has some of this cake!"

CHECKPOINT CHARLIE FRUITCAKE

Robert Keathley has never been what you would call a cautious soul. A few years ago the now-retired schoolteacher flew a small, motorized, ultralight glider over Corsicana and dropped Tootsie Rolls for the kids. It was his one-man equivalent of the Berlin Airlift of 1948.

Back in the early 1960s, when Robert was a young history teacher in Richardson, Texas, he decided he needed to get some firsthand experience with history. So he signed on with the U. S. Department of Defense Overseas Schools as a dormitory counselor. At age 24, he achieved his dream: he was living and working in France.

Not one to be still for long, in late 1963, Robert decided to go to Berlin.

Today, no one thinks twice about making this trip. Back then, it was a different world. Berlin still had four zones of occupation, a vestige of the end of World War II. One zone was American, one French, another British, and the fourth, Russian. That meant a quarter of Berlin was in the hands of the communists, or Soviet Russia.

To the communists went the dubious distinction of the city's other demarcation, the Berlin Wall. The communists had put up the hated wall in August of 1961. It was a grim, often deadly barrier separating West Berlin from East Berlin, western Europe from eastern Europe, freedom from repression. Families were literally divided by the wall, a chilling symbol of the Cold War.

Robert decided then and there he would try to get transferred to Berlin.

"It was an exciting atmosphere," he says. "President Kennedy had just come there, and Americans were really appreciated. I thought my soaking in that experience would make me a better teacher when I returned to the U.S."

Eventually he did get a job in Germany, though not in Berlin, and in 1965 he married a German woman whose father was a colonel in the West German army. She had family she was not allowed to see—a great-uncle and -aunt were trapped in East Berlin.

But Robert could see them. He was an American, and by virtue of his job being under the auspices of the Department of Defense, his passport bore this notice:

THE BEARER IS ABROAD ON AN OFFICIAL ASSIGNMENT
FOR THE UNITED STATES GOVERNMENT.

A Slice of Life

On a cold, wet, gray Berlin day in November of 1965, Robert went to visit Uncle Willie and Aunt Katie. He didn't go empty-handed. Into a large paper sack went delicacies East Berliners seldom saw: two cartons of cigarettes, two pounds of coffee—and a Collin Street Bakery fruitcake. Robert's mother had sent him two fruitcakes, so he decided he'd share.

He brought a can opener, in case the East German guards made him open the can of coffee to see if he had hidden anything inside. He hadn't.

But he prayed they wouldn't check around his belt.

"I had a West German newspaper rolled up vertically that I'd put under my belt in the back. My jacket and coat were hiding it."

Such a seemingly innocuous item was *verboten* in communist Berlin. It would never do for the people of East Germany to read news not government-censored. So the coffee and the Collin Street Bakery fruitcake were not only gifts for his wife's relatives, but also diversions for the guards at Checkpoint Charlie.

Robert had to make his way from Checkpoint Charlie's American guardhouse across the Death Strip, as it was called. It was seventy interminable yards to the East German guardhouse, in full view of two East German watchtowers.

"It all gave me a feeling of the Alamo," Robert says. "I was a bit tense."

Inside the East German checkpoint, Robert dumped out his sack. The guards peered in the coffee can and poked the fruitcake. They stared at the OFFICIAL ASSIGNMENT stamp on his passport. *Down the hall,* they told him. *You must see a higher official.*

Too many cigarettes, the higher official told him, *you must go back.* But the guard didn't let Robert go. Instead, he eyed the fruitcake tin suspiciously. What was this cowboy and a rope? What did it mean?

"That's when I remembered it had been a German baker who invented the Collin Street Bakery fruitcake," Robert says. "Somehow I managed to explain this to him in German."

That seemed to do the trick. The official dismissed Robert. Back to the American guardhouse Robert went, ostensibly to pare down his cigarettes. Then back again across the Death Strip. More pokes and prods to the coffee and the fruitcake.

And then he was in. Uncle Willie and Aunt Katie would get their treats.

"I apologized to my wife's relations for all the holes the guard had made in the fruitcake," Robert says. But the cowboy on the tin had served his purpose, diverting the guards' attention from the newspaper Robert had smuggled in.

When he handed the newspaper to Willie, his wife's great-uncle started to shake. "This is the first Western newspaper I've read in five years," he told Robert.

On another November day, twenty-four years after he'd made it through Checkpoint Charlie, Robert watched on TV as the Berlin Wall came tumbling down. By then he was back in Corsicana, teaching.

"It was an emotional moment," Robert says.

His wife's relations had managed to escape in 1967. Willie never did burn the newspaper Robert brought him, as he should have. "He passed it around to all his friends until it finally fell apart," says Robert.

Robert still has his old passport with the OFFICIAL ASSIGNMENT stamp in it. And he still enjoys the Collin Street Bakery fruitcake, especially the pineapple pecan.

As delicious as it is, though, probably few fruitcakes ever tasted better than the one that got poked, prodded, and successfully spirited through Checkpoint Charlie.

A Daughter's Wish

Herein lies Janet Wakil's tale of the Erie Canal, a speakeasy, a law enforcement official on a first-name basis with smuggling, the frugal meat man, the friendly cookbook writer, and a daughter whose times with a stern father are laced with memories of Collin Street Bakery fruitcakes.

For many years, Janet Wakil worked for her father in the family business, a popular restaurant and banquet facility in Rochester, New York, called The Wishing Well. It was a most respectable place when Janet and her dad ran it, but the building has what's known as a colorful past.

Back in 1919, when the place first opened (and long before Janet's father came on the scene), The Wishing Well was a roadhouse out in the middle of nowhere.

The building itself dated back to 1852, and the basement opened onto a tunnel that led to the Erie Canal, that great connector of commerce that, prophetically, had sparked such songs as this one:

Oh, the Erie's a-rising and the whiskey's gettin' low,
And I hardly think we'll get a drink
Till we get to Buffalo.

That tunnel was more than the not-so-law-abiding local law enforcement officer at the time could have wished for. Prohibition was just going into effect, and the tunnel made it possible to smuggle liquor from nearby Canada through the Erie Canal and into The Wishing Well. (The Erie Canal did, indeed, open up trade between the Buffalo and Albany areas, just like they taught us in the history books. They just didn't tell us the breadth of this exchange.)

On the weekends, The Wishing Well was the restaurant where the local bigwigs brought the wives and kids for the delicious chicken fricassee. Come Monday, the place took on its second life as a speakeasy, where those same local bigwigs returned for the equally tasty whiskey. The difference was that the fricassee was legal, whereas the whiskey was bootlegged.

All that changed when Prohibition ended in 1933. The Wishing Well went back to being a respectable establishment both on the weekends and during the week. The one legacy Janet's dad inherited when he bought the place was a darned good bar.

Not that Mr. Wakil indulged much in its offerings. "My father was a strict disciplinarian and a real taskmaster," says Janet. Her memories are of a father who was all business and little fun.

The one exception was when the Collin Street Bakery fruitcake arrived.

And arrive it did, every year, right after Thanksgiving, the gift of Abe the meat man as a way of thanking Mr. Wakil for buying his restaurant's meat from Abe. What Janet learned later was that thoughtful Abe was also frugal. "He always ordered the smallest of the cakes," she says, laughing.

But never mind—the fruitcake meant one of the few times Janet heard her father laugh. "When it arrived, my father and I would go behind the bar, open the cellophane carefully with scissors, rub our hands, and then proceed to lace the fruitcake with brandy, rum, and sherry," says Janet.

Her father would always reach for the bar liquor—a code name for the cheaper stuff. Janet, however, had other plans for that fruitcake.

"When Dad wasn't looking I'd grab the good stuff—Hennessy, Courvoisier, Harveys. I thought the cake deserved it."

So the little Collin Street fruitcake got a generous dousing of the good stuff. Then Janet and her dad would seal the cake back up and put it back in its tin to let the spirits work their magic and soak through the cake. Over the next few weeks the two would cast longing looks at the tin as they practiced what Janet describes as "extreme self-restraint."

Come Christmas day, there was more laughing and giggling as father and daughter unveiled the fragrant cake and presented it to the family. "When I think back to the rare fun I had with my father, it was almost exclusively over a Collin Street Bakery fruitcake," says Janet.

The years passed and Abe retired and her father died and there were no more fruitcakes. Until a friend of hers, a cookbook writer named Carole Curlee, clued Janet in as to how she could order those same fruitcakes that Abe had sent. (Carole started sending her some—the large ones—to further sweeten their friendship.)

Now, says Janet, "I eat fruitcake for breakfast, lunch, and dinner." And yes, she laces it—with the good stuff.

Janet loves the taste and cherishes the memories. In fact, remembering those rare highs with her father gives her more of a rush than the good stuff ever could.

'TAKE TWO SLICES
AND CALL ME IN THE MORNING'

What some sisters won't do for their little brothers.

For several years, Beverly Tryon and her husband, Mike, have been sending Beverly's three brothers gifts of the Texas Blonde Pecan Cakes. She knew her brothers liked them, but she didn't know just how much her younger brother Joe McAnally appreciated them until recently.

It turns out that Texas Blonde Pecan Cakes are what get Joe through the severe migraines he's struggled with for the past ten years.

The migraines put him off most food, to the point where he has practically no appetite. But during one migraine attack, Joe discovered there was, indeed, one thing that appealed to him.

"I thought, 'I'll try me a little piece of this cake'," says Joe, referring to the Texas Blonde Pecan. "It tasted so good, I decided to try a little more. It was the finest cake I ever put in my mouth."

Joe demolished the cake in two days—every last crumb.

"Joe's wife said she turned around and it was gone," says Beverly, laughing. She'd had no idea how much her gift meant to her brother. "He just happened to mention to me recently that it helped his migraine, and it broke my heart when I heard that. I wished I'd sent him a larger one."

Joe maintains the cake not only tastes good but is good for him as well. "All those fruits and nuts—I'm sure I'm getting nutrients," he says.

At Collin Street Bakery, we make no claims about the curative properties of our cakes. But if they make Joe feel better, we're glad.

Beverly, meanwhile, decided that since she hadn't ordered him the larger cake, she'd sacrifice and send Joe the one she'd ordered for herself. When Joe got the package, it had a big label Beverly had made, describing the contents. It read:

MIGRAINE MEDICINE

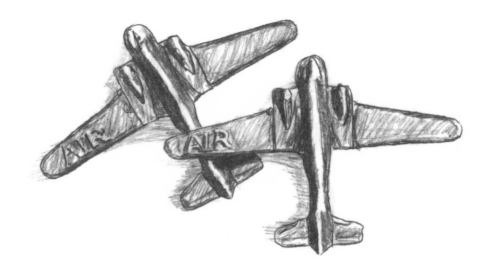

A LOVE AFFAIR TO REMEMBER

She was from Malawi, in Africa, and he was from North Cornwall, in England. Neither of them knew each other. But both of them happened to be flying from Zimbabwe to Malawi on the same January day in 1964 and were seated next to one another on the plane. And so for Maria and Jim, love really did happen at 10,000 feet. They became Mr. and Mrs. James Platt nine months later.

Like so many happy beginnings, it almost didn't happen.

Jim, a mining geologist, was supposed to have flown out of Zimbabwe several days earlier. But a bout with malaria meant he couldn't travel until the day Maria did.

"Malaria is not nice in itself, but it was a blessing to me," says Jim. He and

Maria remained in cloud-nine love long after their first flight.

The two discovered Collin Street Bakery when they and their children were living in Ireland in the late 1970s. "One thing that imprinted itself on my mind was the list of the bakery's celebrity customers, in particular Cary Grant, whose performance I have always admired," says Jim.

He and Maria started sending Collin Street Bakery fruitcakes to family members and friends as Christmas gifts, a tradition they continued year after year. There was always one for their own family as well, which they would cut and share with friends who came to visit.

"We always felt the cakes to be an essential part of the Christmas season," says Jim, "goodness within goodness as it were."

For Maria, that last taste of goodness came in 2007. In July of 2008 she succumbed to cancer. But her husband of almost forty-four years refused to submit to a life without her memory.

New Year's Day is also Maria's birthday. On January 1, 2009, Jim brought a fruitcake to the nurses who had cared for Maria in the chemo ward where she was hospitalized in the Netherlands. The nurses were so touched by the gesture that Jim plans to bring a fruitcake to the ward year after year, on Maria's birthday.

"Cutting the fruitcake in Maria's beloved memory ensures her touch," says Jim. "It will be a new tradition—one in which to take the best of pleasure in holding onto the good memories."

THE THREAD IN THE TAPESTRY

One of the things Suzanne Parnell loves about Collin Street Bakery fruitcake (besides the cherries) is that "it's always there. I've always known I could get one," she says. It's been comfort and continuity.

She first laid eyes on one in 1949, when she was a little girl growing up in Dallas and her aunt sent one to the family. Her mother liked it and started ordering one every year, faithfully. It became a tradition, and traditions in her family were meant to be honored—even when the family was apart.

Suzanne was only 9, but she vividly remembers her mother trying to get a fruitcake to her brother, an Air Force fighter pilot stationed in Korea, in 1951. The politicians called it a police action; the soldiers fighting in it called it a war.

"She was writing letters and on the phone constantly, talking to our Senator's staff, asking how she could get this fruitcake to her son," says Suzanne. The Senator she was dogging was Lyndon Johnson.

"Every morning she got up and called his office until he finally did call back," says Suzanne. "My mama was not giving up!" She got that fruitcake to her son.

Her mother kept up the traditions, not only of the fruitcake but of Christmas in her house. Even when Suzanne and her siblings were grown and had children of their own and had moved away, "by God, you went to Mama's house for Christmas dinner," says Suzanne with a smile.

"The fruitcake was one of the things that held the family together," she says. "It was a thread in the tapestry of family traditions.

"If you lose the traditions," she adds, "you let go of each other." The tapestry unravels.

The traditions went on for many years, but when her mother died they were no more, and Suzanne spent a spate of Christmases without a fruitcake.

A few years ago she became friends with a Texas couple she met at the Arkansas mountaintop retreat she now owns. ("Texans find themselves wherever they go," as she says.) It turned out that Sandy, the husband, worked for Collin Street Bakery.

"I said, 'I know you—you all make fruitcakes. I remember them.'"

Shortly after that, Sandy sent her a fruitcake. In return, Suzanne sent this letter of thanks. She never expected it to be published, but was gracious (and courageous, and wise) enough to allow it to be. It is testimony to the importance of picking up those threads again, and weaving them into that tapestry.

Dear Sandy and Kay,

Your wonderful surprise arrived over a week ago—and it has taken me a while to put into words what it meant to me. When I first saw the box, I was delighted and looked forward to a treat, but I was totally unprepared for what actually happened when I opened the box and saw the Collin Street Bakery logo on the DeLuxe Fruitcake box.

I started crying.

I started crying as a flood of memories washed over me, beginning with the last time I had seen a Collin Street Fruitcake. That was Christmas, 1987, the last Christmas my Mother felt up to traveling from Dallas to my family's Christmas in Arkansas. I made sure we had a CS Fruitcake for her that year because, well, that's what we had always had at Christmas when she was "matriarch in charge." Then I began to remember all the Christmases back through the years with a fruitcake from Collin Street always on the table. I seemed to remember highlighted years in reverse order, with each one surfacing gradually such as Christmas, 1980, the one before my father's death (September, '81), and the last Christmas the whole family was together.

So many years, so many memories. It was an emotional trip backward through time until I laughed as I remembered the crucial year that set the CS Fruitcake firmly in family lore—1951, when my brother was a fighter pilot in Korea and my mother was obsessed with getting one of those fruitcakes to him in time for Christmas. And there was 1949, the beginning of it all. That year my Aunt Amelia (my father's sister) sent us a Collin Street Fruitcake for Christmas because she was out of the country and could not shop as usual. The tradition for my branch of the family began then, and for years my Aunt sent us the Collin Street Fruitcake no matter what else she sent.

So I cried with all the memories. I still cry a little at times when I glance at it on the counter—or write about it as here. It isn't sadness; it's nostalgia, and a kind of wonder at it all. I don't know if I will be able to eat the Fruitcake after all of this, certainly not until Christmas.

"It's just a fruitcake," you say. But it isn't. It went far beyond being a "fruitcake" the year my mother moved heaven and earth and the military to get that fruitcake to my brother in time for Christmas. Everybody learned that year my mother was a force to be reckoned with, and the Collin Street Fruitcake became a lifeline to home, a statement of love, a symbol of the family unity, an anchor to the heart and hearth of our family. And it continued to be that year after year after year.

To my surprise it remains so today in my heart. Years after my mother and father have died, years since the family has had any cohesion, years since I have had a fruitcake of any kind at Christmas, I learned, because of your gift, that the Collin Street Fruitcake is a tangible symbol of my family's life—of my life. It is a motif that links Christmases, people, times, events, feelings—the memories of thirty-plus years together in one tangible object, one recognizable product made with quality and care and tradition.

I don't know if other people have these experiences with those amazing Fruitcakes, or if like me, they don't know a motif or a "memory sink" when they eat one. But the truth is, one day years later some of those who have years of Collin Street tradition will see the logo or someone will send them a CS Fruitcake, and the unexpected will happen as it did with me. The experiences of their lives will coalesce around The Fruitcake that was always on the sideboard at Christmas—and they will remember.

I realize now I have lost something of my history and my heart by not actively continuing the tradition. I plan to change that this year. I plan to send my sister and my brother a Collin Street Fruitcake. They will remember, perhaps they will cry. And I plan to begin sending one to my son, who will have his own child soon. He will remember the fruitcake from his grandmother's Christmases; perhaps he will cry too—or perhaps not, being younger and not given to nostalgia quite yet. But I will tell him how important it is to build traditions and anchor them in tangible objects that become triggers in good ways in years to come. I will tell him how hard it is to find people like Collin Street Bakery who have the "legs" to be here so people like us can build our traditions with delicious products that span the days of our lives. The company spans my lifetime; its products have helped me define and hold the memories of that lifetime. That is huge. Thank you for opening that understanding.

Please tell the people at Collin Street Bakery they are more important than they can possibly imagine in our throw-away, here-today, gone-tomorrow world. People still need traditions. Our hearts still need tangible ways to hold our memories. It is important to know that some companies, some people make products and logos capable of forging links to the times of our lives and to those memories, that some companies have the power to root a society in its history. Collin Street Bakery is one of those, maybe the only one left.

Thank you again,

Suzanne

AN ANTARCTIC FEAST

On that vast, frozen canvas of ice called Antarctica is a volcanic island off the Antarctic Peninsula with an accessible harbor. But as Jorge Iturriago of Santiago, Chile, discovered the year he lived there, there was a reason why it was called Deception Island.

"We thought it was a dead volcano," says Jorge. "Big mistake."

It was 1967, and Jorge was working as the head of the Chilean Station there. Chile was one of three countries to have an outpost on this most out-of-the-way place on the earth. England and Argentina were also there. The three groups were all friendly with one another and often visited with each other. But on December 4th they all got a jolt—literally. The so-called dead volcano came to ferocious life, its eruption partially destroying all three stations. Fortunately, all the people were rescued.

Up until that point it had been a pretty quiet year—there are, after all, only so many things you can do in Antarctica. That's why Jorge and the other people stationed there decided to throw a midwinter celebration…on June 21st. In the northern hemisphere, people were celebrating the first day of summer on that day. But on Deception Island, winter was in full swing.

"In the latitude where we stayed—62 degrees South—the daylight started about 10 a.m., and it finished about 4 p.m.," says Jorge. "We saw the sun just a little bit above the horizon at midday. The temperature at this latitude was about 23 degrees Centigrade below zero. Of course," he adds, "at the South Pole it is much colder."

The British station decided to host the bash. But what do you serve at such a party? It's not like you can run out to the grocery store.

"At that time, the only way to get to Antarctica was by ship during the summer," says Jorge. "We took all our food and supplies by ship. After the summer we did not have any opportunity to get anything until the following year."

Fortunately one of the English fellows, John, had planned ahead. Before he shipped out for Antarctica from England, his wife gave him a special cake just for the midwinter festival. Some relatives living in Texas had sent it to her.

And so on June 21st all the temporary Antarcticans gathered around as John ceremoniously opened the box and cut a piece of cake for everyone.

"That was the first time I tasted Collin Street Bakery fruitcake," says Jorge.

"For me it was a great experience, because I had never before tasted a cake kept in a box for so long a time, that kept its wonderful, delicious flavor."

Years later, when Jorge was back living in Santiago, a brochure arrived from Collin Street Bakery. "I remembered immediately that Antarctic cake," he says. He ordered one for his family, then for his friends, and has been doing so ever since. None of them go to Deception Island, but for Jorge, they still taste as good as they did at Latitude 62 degrees South.

A Little Bit About the Bakery

You could no more take Collin Street Bakery out of Corsicana than you could take the star out of the Texas flag. Ever since master baker August Weidmann carried his recipe for fruitcake from Weisbaden, Germany, to America in 1896, our bakery has been a part of Corsicana. (The current Seventh Street address is just four blocks from the original location.)

We try to always honor the values of home and family and good neighbors that one associates with America's small towns, of which Corsicana is, in our view, among the finest. At the same time, our bakery has attracted an international clientele almost from the beginning. We have Mr. John Ringling's famous circus troupe to thank for that.

In the early 1900s, they were among the travelers who stayed in the hotel that used to be above the bakery. Mr. Weidmann's business partner, the born marketer Tom McElwee, used to tuck a fruitcake in the luggage of departing guests as a delicious reminder of their stay. The Ringling circus members found theirs once they got to their next destination—Europe. They shared the fruitcake with friends there, who clamored for more. And so Collin Street Bakery began shipping fruitcakes all over the world.

We're proud to say our fruitcake has delighted royalty and diplomats, Hollywood legends and sports stars—and thousands of families in America and beyond, often for generations. Collin Street Bakery fruitcakes have been a welcome taste of home.

In the 1940s my grandfather, Lee McNutt, and great-uncle Bob Rutherford purchased Collin Street Bakery, with the help of their good friend and partner Harry Cook, from the widow of one of the founders. Along with the Lamar Hunt Family, who became partners in the 1960s, the Cook and McNutt families are still partners today. My brother Bill, my sisters Katherine and Melanie, and I all worked here growing up. My first job was folding boxes for the bake shop.

The McNutts are just one of many families who have worked at the bakery for generations. Even today, you'll find the children and grandchildren of earlier workers. Most of them grew up here in Corsicana.

And lots of the folks who work here have staying power. Maurice Pollock was one. He started as a delivery boy in 1931, working alongside his father. Maurice retired as Vice President and Treasurer of Collin Street Bakery sixty-six years later, at the age of 83.

In addition to Maurice, I have had the privilege of working with Jerry Grimmett, our longest-serving Vice President (fifty-five years), Norman Shaw, our Executive Vice President and partner (thirty-five years), and John Crawford, who joined us as a partner in the 1960s. His son Hayden is our most recent new partner.

We are probably one of the few companies in America whose products have been enjoyed on all seven continents—Antarctica included. We ship more fruitcake to more places than any other bakery in the country, and we bake about a million a year. Our recipe is a carefully guarded secret, but one secret we're happy to share is that pecans make up more than one-fourth of our fruitcake's ingredients by weight.

We go to great lengths to obtain the finest ingredients—from shelling our own pecans here in Texas to raising our own organic pineapple in Costa Rica. It's how we make the finest products for the finest, most loyal customers on the planet.

In 2006, Collin Street Bakery celebrated another milestone. We opened our first freestanding bakery store, on Highway 287 and I-45, just outside Corsicana. We've since opened a second store outside of Waco. In the years to come you will see more of these stores along Texas highways. Their wide front porches are a symbol to travelers of the hospitality that awaits every customer of Collin Street Bakery.

> Please visit Collin Street Bakery on the Web at
> www.collinstreet.com
> and come see us when you can.

Cordially,

Bob McNutt, President
and the staff of COLLIN STREET BAKERY

P.S. We always love to hear our customers' stories. Feel free to drop us a line, or e-mail us at service@collinstreet.com.

To: The Makers of the Best
Fruit Cake in the World,

TEXAS,

U.S.A.

Fruitcake
Corsicana texas

75110/9999

Fruit Cake C
Texas

To Nancy Lu.
San Jose Ca. 95127

Texas Fruitcake
Texas

CH 40027

Worlds Greatest
Fruit Cakes
Corsicana, Texas

Fruitcake
Texas

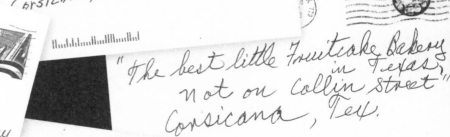

Golden street Bakery
Corsicana
Texas 7510

75110/9999

"The best little Fruitcake Bakery
in Texas,
not on Collin street"
Corsicana, Tex.

Iowa

527

STATES ARMY

fruitake place
Corsicana, TEXAS

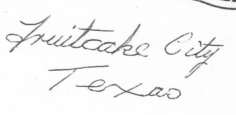

Fruitcake City
Texas

S0-AGU-615

Tough Cookie

Tough Cookie

Written by Kate Louise
Illustrated by Grace Sandford

Sky Pony Press
New York

For my family, for being won-dough-ful. —K. L.

For my mum and dad, thank you for everything. —G. S.

This is no ordinary gingerbread man. He is missing a very important ingredient. You might even say it's the most important ingredient of all.

Without ginger, the gingerbread man
feels like he's not really a gingerbread
man at all.

He can't be sold in the bakery, so he
lives in the back of the store and
causes all kinds of trouble . . .

"He he!" the gingerbread man squeals
as he squirts frosting on the walls.
"I need that for my cupcakes!" the baker yells.

"Ha ha!" the gingerbread man giggles as he stuffs candy into his mouth.

"I need those to decorate the cookies!" the baker says angrily.

"Woo hoo!" the gingerbread man cheers as he scatters sprinkles across the counter.

"I need those for the donuts!" the baker shouts.

Before long, the baker has had enough of the
gingerbread man's mischief and orders him to leave.

"You are upsetting the other gingerbread men and women,
and you are ruining my business!" the baker scolds.

"But I don't want to leave!"
the gingerbread man cries.

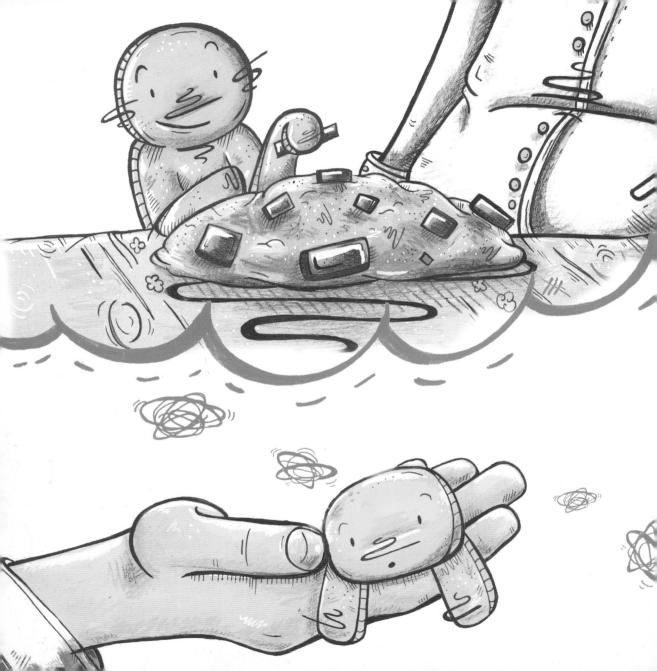

So the baker teaches the gingerbread man that niceness comes from him, not from whether he has the right ingredients.

"Being kind makes others feel good and will make you happy, too," the baker says.

So instead of eating the yummy gummy buttons, the gingerbread man helps the baker decorate the other gingerbread men and women.

Oooh!

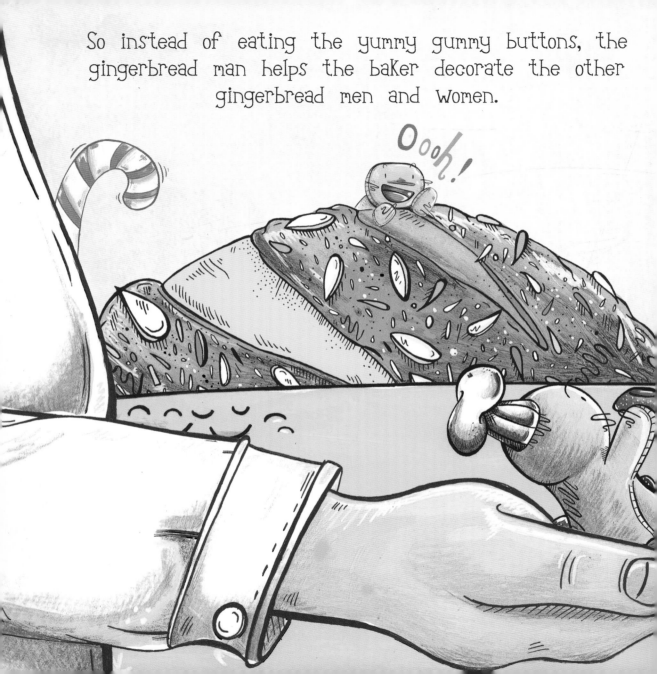

And instead of squeezing frosting on the walls and shaking sprinkles everywhere, the gingerbread man helps the baker decorate his cakes and donuts.

The gingerbread man sifts the flour

...and rolls the dough

...and uses the cookie cutter to make new friends.

The gingerbread man helps the other
gingerbread men and women on their journey
from oven to bakery shelf.

And he always makes sure
to add the ginger!

Text copyright © 2015 by Kate Louise

Illustration copyright © 2015 by Grace Sandford

All rights reserved. No part of this book may be reproduced in any manner without the express written consent of the publisher, except in the case of brief excerpts in critical reviews or articles. All inquiries should be addressed to Sky Pony Press, 307 West 36th Street, 11th Floor, New York, NY 10018.

Sky Pony Press books may be purchased in bulk at special discounts for sales promotion, corporate gifts, fund-raising, or educational purposes. Special editions can also be created to specifications. For details, contact the Special Sales Department, Sky Pony Press, 307 West 36th Street, 11th Floor, New York, NY 10018 or info@skyhorsepublishing.com.

Sky Pony® is a registered trademark of Skyhorse Publishing, Inc.®, a Delaware corporation.

Visit our website at www.skyponypress.com.

10 9 8 7 6 5 4 3 2 1

Manufactured in China, June 2015

This product conforms to CPSIA 2008

Library of Congress Cataloging-in-Publication Data is available on file.

Cover design and illustrations by Grace Sandford

Print ISBN: 978-1-63450-197-2

Ebook ISBN: 978-1-63450-924-4